To Dear Joan,
On the occasion
80th Birthday.
With much love,
Meg + Lorraine.

KANGAROOS & WALLABIES
of Australia

DAVE WATTS

NEW HOLLAND

KANGAROOS & WALLABIES
of Australia

DAVE WATTS

First published in 1998 by
New Holland Publishers (Australia) Pty Ltd
Sydney • Cape Town • London

14 Aquatic Drive
Frenchs Forest, NSW 2086
Australia

80 McKenzie Street
Cape Town 8001
South Africa

24 Nutford Place
London W1H 6DQ
United Kingdom

National Library Cataloguing-in-Publication Data:
    Watts, Dave
    Kangaroos and wallabies of Australia.

    Includes index.
    ISBN 1 86436 320 7.

    1. Kangaroos — Australia. 2. Wallabies — Australia. I.
    Title.

    599.220994

Publishing general manager: Jane Hazell
Publisher: Averill Chase
Editors: Anouska Good, Jacquie Brown
Designer: Laurence Lemmon-Warde
DTP cartographer: Laurence Lemmon-Warde
Consultant: Dr M.B. Bennett, Department of Anatomical Sciences,
                University of Queensland

Reproduction by Hirt & Carter Cape (Pty) Ltd
Printed and bound in Singapore by Tien Wah Press (Pte) Ltd

HALF-TITLE PAGE Adult male Red Kangaroo relaxing.
TITLE PAGE Forester Kangaroos on Maria Island, Tasmania.
THIS PAGE A juvenile Eastern Grey Kangaroo.
ACKNOWLEDGEMENTS PAGE Female Red Kangaroo in mid hop.
CONTENTS PAGE Mother and juvenile Bennett's Wallabies.
PAGES 10–11 Eastern Grey Kangaroo grazing in a swamp.

ACKNOWLEDGEMENTS

It would be impossible to work on a book such as this without the help and support of so many people from all over Australia.

In particular I could not have obtained photographs of several kangaroo species without the help of various officers of the National Parks and Wildlife Service.

I wish to thank the many officers of the Queensland Department of the Environment including Chris Evenson, Claire Smith and Peter McCrae at the Charleville Office; Peter Johnson at Pallarenda; Laurie Pitt at Taunton Scientific Reserve; Tom Mumbray at the Brisbane office; and Colin and Maureen Morgan, Janelle Lowry, Jess Hemmings and Jane Haxton at Idalia National Park. To Alan and Christine Horsup, thank you for your continuing support and hospitality over the years.

My sincere gratitude to those officers of the Tasmanian Parks and Wildlife Service who have given so much help for many years including Jamie Bayley-Stark, Nick Mooney, Peter Brown, Mark Holdsworth, Greg Hocking, Steven Smith, Sally Bryant and Stewart Blackhall. I wish to thank the rangers in the field in Tasmania including Jans and Katina Howe, Gary Sutton, David Montgomery, Brian Carson, Mary Anne Austin and Ian Marmion.

A special thank you to Geoff Underwood and Simone at Tidbinbilla Nature Reserve for their help and kindness. I am very grateful to David Croft and Lisa Silva for pointing me in the right direction and allowing me to photograph at Fowler's Gap Research Station. My sincere thanks to John Chambers for allowing me access to his rainforest creatures near Lake Eatcham.

To the staff of Healesville Sanctuary who have helped so much, including Diane Logg and Kevin Mason, a special thank you. My deepest gratitude goes to the staff at Yookamurra Sanctuary where Mick McCracken, Tim Bale and Lynne Pope are demonstrating what a magnificent habitat mallee really is. I would also like to thank Stephen Reilly and Craig Alders for trusting me to photograph the Brush-tailed Rock-wallabies near the Jenolan Caves. My sincere thanks go to Mike Jagoe and staff at Talune Wildlife Park for their continuing help and support.

I owe a debt to Paul Sargeant who has given considerable help towards publicity, a special thanks to Julie Sargeant for assisting with photographic equipment and to Fionná Sargeant-Gilbert for her enthusiastic support. I gratefully acknowledge the loving help and support given to me by Helen Sargeant and for tolerating the long hours I have spent working on this book.

Finally it has been a great pleasure working with the staff at New Holland Publishers. Special thanks to Gerry Struik, Jane Hazell, Averill Chase, Anouska Good, Laurence Lemmon-Warde, and Bronwyn Rennex for their tireless support in bringing this project to fruition.

Dave Watts
Kettering, Tasmania

CONTENTS

INTRODUCTION

It is difficult to imagine the Australian continent without the kangaroo, a treasured icon that appears on the country's coat of arms. The kangaroo's combination of grace, beauty, efficiency and speed symbolises for many the essence of wild Australia; while its bounding motion and unique appearance — upright stance, long powerful hind legs, long tail, joey in the pouch — make it immediately recognisable to locals and visitors alike.

The largest marsupials living today are the true kangaroos. These are the six largest species of the family of macropods (meaning 'big foot'). The other family members are the smaller wallabies which, along with the kangaroos, can be grouped together with the rat-kangaroos and potoroos into one large superfamily — the macropodoidea. While the bigger kangaroos and wallabies are easily recognisable macropods, many of the smaller members, such as potoroos or bettongs, may not be instantly recognised as relatives because they are small and spend much of their time on all fours. They are, however, all macropods with long feet and the ability to hop.

Kangaroos are all essentially grazing animals that prefer open woodlands and wide open plains. They and the closely related larger wallabies are all sexually dimorphic — the males of the species are considerably larger than the females. This is particularly marked in the larger kangaroos and is a result of their complex social system based on male dominance — the larger and stronger the male, the more successful he is going to be at passing on his genes.

The name 'wallaby' is a fairly loose term. It is generally applied to any macropod species that weighs less than 20 kilograms as an adult. Larger wallabies, such as the Red-necked Wallaby, are nocturnal creatures with a more varied feeding system than that of the predominantly grazing kangaroos; they browse on selected shrubs of the understorey as well as grazing both native and introduced grasses in cleared areas.

Some of the most beautiful of all macropods are the rock-wallabies, of which approximately 10 species still exist today. Particularly striking is the Yellow-footed Rock-wallaby whose unusual colouring is a camouflage adaptation allowing it to remain unseen in its open rocky habitat. This helps it to avoid the prying eyes of the Wedge-tailed Eagle.

Origins

Until recently the fossil record of kangaroos was largely unknown. However, discoveries by researchers from the University of New South Wales who have been working at the Riversleigh fossil site in north-western Queensland since the mid-1970s have provided some answers to previous mysteries of macropod evolution.

Scientists are now convinced that the evolution of macropods began in the forests of the supercontinent of Gondwana around 150 million years ago. This was still the age of dinosaurs and Australia was connected — along with India, Africa and South America — to what is now Antarctica. Massive movements in the earth's crust caused Gondwana to break up, with separate pieces drifting across the globe to eventually form new continents. The first to break away was Africa, followed by India about 100 million years ago. By 40 million years ago Australia had split from Antarctica and was beginning to drift northward. The oldest marsupial fossils were discovered in South America and primitive marsupials still live there today,

OPPOSITE The granulated soles of the feet of this Black-footed Rock-wallaby aid in gripping slippery rock surfaces.

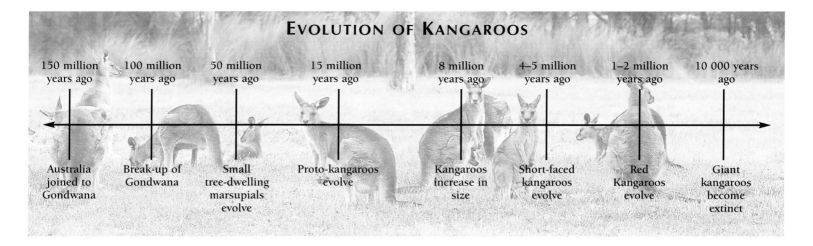

EVOLUTION OF KANGAROOS

150 million years ago	100 million years ago	50 million years ago	15 million years ago	8 million years ago	4–5 million years ago	1–2 million years ago	10 000 years ago
Australia joined to Gondwana	Break-up of Gondwana	Small tree-dwelling marsupials evolve	Proto-kangaroos evolve	Kangaroos increase in size	Short-faced kangaroos evolve	Red Kangaroos evolve	Giant kangaroos become extinct

together with plant species including conifers, cycads and tree ferns, which are closely related to similar Australian plants such as the recently discovered Wollemi pine, a type of conifer.

As Australia drifted northward with its primitive marsupials, flowering plants began to evolve alongside the primeval forests of podocarps, conifers and tree ferns. The nutritious nectar and pollen and the rich feast of insects attracted by the flowers enabled the mainly tree-dwelling omnivorous marsupials to thrive and multiply.

From 30 to 50 million years ago, much of mainland Australia was covered by rainforest and the rainfall was far higher than today. During the period between 25 and five million years ago, the inland was still covered by rainforest, large lake systems and many slow-flowing rivers. Approximately 15 million years ago, several forms of possum- and koala-like marsupials abandoned

their arboreal lifestyle and became ground dwellers. It has been deduced from the shape of their fossilised foot bones that these earliest ancestors of kangaroos could not hop, but progressed on all fours. The prehensile tail, useful for grasping branches in an arboreal lifestyle, evolved to become a support or balance while hopping. Mostly small in size, these proto-kangaroos (as the early ancestors of kangaroos are called) were omnivorous and lived on a diet of insects, fruit, fungi, worms and small vertebrates, similar to the feeding habits of the bettongs, potoroos and brush-tail possums of today.

As Australia continued to drift north into warmer latitudes the climate became progressively drier. Around eight million years ago the vast expanse of rainforest began to retract to the coastal margins. The five-toed Musky Rat-kangaroo, *Hypsiprymnodon moschatus*, which still remains widespread in the rainforest of northern Queensland, is the most primitive of all present-day kangaroos. The first toe of each hind foot (which is similar to that of possums) and its diet of fallen fruit, insects and earthworms demonstrate its direct descent from the proto-kangaroos of this time.

Gradually these kangaroos grew larger and expanded their diet to include leaves and shoots of shrubs and herbs. Around this time, the second and third toes on each hind foot began to diminish in size. The resulting foot, with a large, strong fourth toe and somewhat smaller fifth toe, was particularly suitable for a hopping style of locomotion. However, due to time-consuming feeding habits, which left them little time to develop social structures, these proto-kangaroos were solitary creatures.

Representing the next rung on the ladder of kangaroo evolution is the Rufous Bettong, *Aepyprymnus rufescens*, which also remains common in parts of Queensland today. The proto-kangaroos had evolved to include groups of animals very similar to present-day bettongs and potoroos, with more efficient digestive systems able to process bulkier plant material. A refined hopping motion began to emerge which allowed them to utilise their front paws to reach and grasp food such as leafy branches which would otherwise have been inaccessible.

As the Australian climate warmed, so in turn the landscape changed; the lakes dried up and retreating rainforest gave way to drier woodland with open grassy plains. The kangaroo family now began to expand. Some forest wallabies evolved more advanced digestive systems and teeth better suited to eating grass. The nocturnal Red-necked Wallabies, *Macropus rufogriseus*, which are abundant in parts of south-eastern Australia and Tasmania, show some characteristics of these transitional creatures. They are able to browse selectively on bushes and shrubs, but also graze in more open areas before returning to the cover of the woodland for security during the day.

Some of the larger forms of kangaroo then evolved longer and more powerful hind legs which allowed them to maintain rapid hopping for extended periods. Their tails also became longer and more powerful — acting as a balance during speed hopping or as a support while sitting, moving slowly or during boxing bouts with rival males. This hopping motion is a distinctive and unique feature not found among any other large animals alive today.

As kangaroos moved from living in forests to a life on the open plains, they became more social and formed groups — several pairs of eyes are more efficient than one at spotting danger, enabling the group to hop swiftly to safety. Studies at Harvard University have shown that, particularly at medium- to high-speed, hopping is far more energy efficient than an equivalent-sized placental mammal running on all fours. The Red Kangaroo, *Macropus rufus*, represents the culmination of this evolution and adaptation — these elegant kangaroos are able to maintain speeds of 20 to 30 kilometres per hour for prolonged periods across the vast outback plains, and can hop at speeds of around 55 kilometres per hour in short bursts. At low speeds (less than about five kilometres per hour) kangaroos do not hop but progress in a slow walk using their tails as a support, rather like a fifth leg.

The Red Kangaroo is the most recently evolved kangaroo; its fossil record does not extend back beyond the Pleistocene

ABOVE   A Bennett's Wallaby relaxes on the rainforest edge in Cradle Mountain–Lake St Clair National Park, Tasmania.
OPPOSITE   The five-toed Musky Rat-kangaroo inhabits the rainforest floor of north-eastern Queensland.

ABOVE This hopping male Red Kangaroo is a typical sight on the wide arid plains of inland Australia.
OPPOSITE A Red-legged Pademelon emerges from the rainforest during late afternoon to feed on leaves and fruit.

Epoch of two million to 10 000 years ago. Indeed, this majestic and graceful inhabitant of the dunes and plains of recent Australia has come a long way from its small marsupial ancestor, once confined to hunting for insects and worms on the forest floor of the ancient Gondwana supercontinent.

During the Pleistocene, the earth experienced great climatic fluctuations as huge ice sheets expanded and retreated from the polar regions. The sea levels rose as ice melted, and fell again as water became locked in ice. At the height of glaciation Australia's highest mountains were covered by ice and glaciers, and Tasmania was connected to the mainland. During this period Australia's deserts grew larger than they are now, creating vast, arid dunefields. The rapidly changing conditions led to the evolution of many new kinds of kangaroo, such as nailtail wallabies, hare-wallabies and the Red Kangaroos — all arid country specialists. Many unusual types of kangaroo flourished during this period including several species of giant kangaroo which are now extinct.

The genus *Procoptodon* includes the largest kangaroo species that ever lived, which was restricted to the Pleistocene. *Procoptodons* had short faces similar to the unusual sthenurine, or short-faced, kangaroos that had begun to appear during the earlier Pliocene Epoch about five to two million years ago. These giant kangaroos probably weighed up to 300 kilograms and differed from the sthenurines in that their teeth had adapted to suit a more grazing lifestyle. Studies conducted in the Menindee region of New South Wales have unearthed an abundance of giant kangaroo fossils which have revealed that they had particularly long and mobile forearms and that two of their five fingers were elongated with two long claws.

Towards the end of the Pleistocene, numerous large animals worldwide, including many kangaroo species in Australia, were hit by a wave of extinctions. This coincided with the arrival of early human beings in the Americas and Australia, suggesting that the large herbivores and their predators were unable to cope with the new arrivals and were hunted to extinction. Species that vanished include the giant ancestors of present-day grey kangaroos and the ferocious Marsupial Lion, *Thylacoleo carniflex*, which was a major predator of kangaroos at this time but which also became extinct about 17 000 years ago.

Humans can be extremely efficient hunters, even if they are only armed with simple weapons such as spears or clubs. Similar mass extinctions of megafauna coincided with humans arriving in New Zealand and Madagascar 1000 years ago, and in North America 11 000 years ago. We know from recently discovered Palaeolithic art in Chauvet Cave, southern France, that rhinoceros, lion and giant deer survived there 30 000 years ago. However, 15 000 years later these species had vanished from southern Europe indicating that our vision of early humans as being in tune with their environment may not be as idyllic as we had hoped. Within Australia all animals over about 70 kilograms were wiped out, leaving Red and grey kangaroos as the largest native land species alive on the continent today.

The arrival of Europeans in Australia in the late-18th century once again led to widespread extinctions. This time the casualties were mainly limited to the smaller species. Among the species lost were the Crescent Nailtail Wallaby, *Onychogalea lunata*; the pretty Toolache Wallaby, *Macropus greyi*; and the Eastern Hare-wallaby, *Lagorchestes leporides*. At the time of European settlement the Toolache Wallaby was abundant in scrub areas of south-eastern South Australia but was persecuted relentlessly because of its fine fur and its fast gait, which provided 'good sport' for the settlers. The last of these animals were killed during the early 1920s.

An Amazing Diversity

The incredible diversity of size and form of kangaroos and wallabies is a source of continuing wonder and study for amateurs and professionals alike. Australia's macropods are adept at occupying a wide range of terrestrial habitats including rainforest, dry woodland, dense swamps and arid deserts. There are kangaroos that live high in rainforest trees, some that scuttle across the rainforest floor, those that are able to dig deep and complex burrows and, of course, most are able to hop on their hind legs for long distances, seemingly without tiring.

Rainforest Dwellers

Rainforest represents one of the oldest habitats in Australia. It now only exists as isolated patches occupying about 0.3 per cent of Australia's total land area, mainly in highland regions of the east coast. This incredibly rich habitat extends to nearly two million hectares. The kangaroos found here are also of ancient ancestry, including the unique Musky Rat-kangaroo which, at about 500 grams, is the smallest living macropod.

Two species of pademelon also inhabit rainforest and other wet forest areas: the Red-necked Pademelon, *Thylogale thetis*; and the Red-legged Pademelon, *Thylogale stigmatica*. These species remain common in suitable forest areas close to the eastern coastal seaboard.

The only other macropods found in rainforests are the two unusual and unique tree kangaroo species; Lumholtz's Tree-kangaroo, *Dendrolagus lumholzi*; and Bennett's Tree-kangaroo, *Dendrolagus bennettianus*, which are only found in far north-eastern Queensland. There are approximately 10 tree-kangaroo species in the world — all except the two abovementioned species are found in Papua New Guinea. Unusually, tree-kangaroos appear to have evolved from ground-dwelling kangaroos which returned to an arboreal existence. Although residing high in rainforest trees, tree-kangaroos are poorly adapted to an arboreal lifestyle and are not particularly agile, which makes food gathering somewhat precarious.

ABOVE The Bennett's Wallaby of Tasmania has evolved long and dense fur to survive the cold alpine winters.

BELOW This adult female Tasmanian Pademelon is able to regulate, by flexing strong muscles, the amount of time the joey spends in the pouch each day.

Forest, Woodland and Scrub Dwellers

The greatest proportion of kangaroo and wallaby species are found in forests, woodland and scrub which cover vast areas of eastern, southern and south-western Australia. In some regions of eastern Australia there is a great diversity of habitats ranging from tall and dry forests to brigalow scrub and heathland, where up to 10 species of kangaroo and wallaby live in close proximity, each species adapted to utilising differing habitats and food resources.

Certain species, such as the Eastern Grey Kangaroo and the Red-necked Wallaby are able to exist in a huge range of habitat types. Red-necked Wallabies are equally at home in coastal heathland, dry sclerophyll forest or even high alpine areas. Other inhabitants of the eastern forested country include the shy Swamp Wallaby, *Wallabia bicolor*; the rare Parma Wallaby, *Macropus parma*; and the Tasmanian Pademelon, *Thylogale billardierii*. The Western Brush Wallaby, *Macropus irma*, is restricted to south-western Western Australia.

Forests of tropical regions are home to a range of macropods that are not found in southern areas, such as the large

Antilopine Wallaroo, *Macropus antilopinus*; Northern Nailtail Wallaby, *Onychogalea unguifera*; and the nervous and alert Agile Wallaby, *Macropus agilis*.

Among the smaller wallaby species at home in forests and woodlands are the Long-nosed Potoroo, *Potorous tridactylus*; the rare and only recently discovered Long-footed Potoroo, *Potorous longipes*; the Tasmanian Bettong, *Bettongia gaimardi*; and the Rufous Bettong, *Aepyprymnus rufescens*. Both species of bettong prefer grassy, open forests and woodland.

Inhabiting the forests and heaths of south-western Western Australia and Rottnest Island is one of the most primitive of macropods, the Quokka, *Setonix brachyurus*.

Rocky Habitat Dwellers

Rocky hills and outcrops offer caves, overhangs and crevices for security and these habitats, often surrounded by dense woodland or scrub, have been colonised by another group of wallabies — the rock-wallabies, of which there are approximately 10 species. Although several species such as the Brush-tailed Rock-wallaby, *Petrogale penicillata*, occur in the wetter eastern areas, some species such as the Yellow-footed Rock-wallaby, *Petrogale xanthopus*, and Black-footed Rock-wallaby, *Petrogale lateralis*, are found on rocky outcrops or gorges of the more arid areas of central Australia.

Another inhabitant of rocky country or gorges is the Common Wallaroo, or Euro, *Macropus robustus*, a large, heavily built and shaggy-coated kangaroo. Sheltering by day in caves or under rock ledges often high on a rocky hill or escarpment, these marsupials venture onto lower country and plains to feed during late afternoon.

Kangaroos of Arid Australia

Arid areas of Australia are among the most forbidding of environments, yet several kangaroo species have adapted to these conditions. Red Kangaroos, *Macropus rufus*, rely on shade during the day to avoid intense solar radiation and feed mainly at night. They are very much an integral feature of the inland open plains, but are also found within some woodland areas.

One of the most unusual inhabitants of desert regions is the Burrowing Bettong, or Boodie, *Bettongia lesueur*, which is a rabbit-sized macropod with a banded tail. This macropod species digs a deep and complex system of burrows to escape the high temperatures above ground.

TOP The Swamp Wallaby is an extremely wary macropod.
ABOVE The colourful markings of this male Yellow-footed Rock-wallaby enable him to blend into the environment.

DIET

As well as occupying a broad spectrum of habitats, modern-day kangaroos and wallabies have also evolved a variety of feeding techniques, enabling them to exploit underground tubers, fruit, seeds, bark, fungi, and insects.

Many species are able to eat grass, including the six large kangaroo species (which are almost purely grazing animals); all of the larger wallabies such as the Red-necked Wallaby and Agile Wallaby; the rock-wallabies; and some of the smaller species such as the Rufous Bettong, Spectacled Hare-wallaby (*Lagorchestes conspicillatus*), Quokka and the pademelons.

Most macropods (with the exception of potoroos and bettongs), have a large sac-like structure attached to the front of the stomach. This structure holds many millions of tiny single-celled bacteria that can digest the cellulose of grass and leaves which the kangaroos are otherwise unable to break down. The nutrients trapped inside the plant cells are then released by the micro-organisms into the macropod stomach. Sheep, cattle, deer and antelopes have evolved a similar symbiotic relationship with bacteria enabling them to digest cellulose and plant fibre more easily.

Rainforest-inhabiting tree-kangaroos face many problems obtaining sufficient nutrients from high in the canopy where most of the available food, such as leaves and shoots, is found far out on the ends of branches. An

LEFT   Many macropods, like this Agile Wallaby, are able to hold food in their forepaws while eating.

OPPOSITE TOP   Eastern Grey Kangaroos are essentially grazing animals, although they do browse on specific types of shrub.

OPPOSITE BOTTOM   This sub-adult male Western Grey Kangaroo is selecting particular herbs in preference to others.

exception is the Musky Rat-kangaroo, an omnivore which is able to feast on a variety of fruits and seeds that fall to the rainforest floor, as well as whatever insects it can find.

Many of the smaller wallabies such as bettongs and potoroos have an acute sense of smell which, together with powerful forefeet used in digging, enables them to exploit food buried within the soil and leaf litter, such as roots, tubers and fungi. In fact, Tasmanian Bettongs live almost exclusively on small underground fungi which proliferate in dry open woodlands, especially following bush fires.

By far the greatest number of kangaroo and wallaby species are opportunistic and selective browsers, feeding on shoots and leaves of bushes and small trees wherever they are within reach. While standing on their hind legs, many macropods use their forepaws to reach, grasp and pull down branches that would otherwise be out of reach.

Kangaroos and wallabies of the vast arid regions of Australia have adapted to survive and many evolved remarkable ways to achieve this. Red Kangaroos and Euros can exist on very little water — the Red Kangaroo requires water in similar amounts to a camel, approximately one-quarter of the water needed by sheep or goats. The kidneys of arid zone kangaroos have

concentrating abilities far in excess of those of placental mammals and some kangaroos are able to obtain all of their water requirements from plant food.

The Tammar Wallaby, *Macropus eugenii*, is able to drink seawater and some kangaroos have been seen eating seaweed. In spite of these adaptations to survive in arid landscapes, kangaroos do still require water and the provision of dams and bores for watering stock has allowed some kangaroo populations in the outback to thrive.

ABOVE The kangaroo was, and remains, an integral part of the Dreamtime of Australian Aboriginal people.
OPPOSITE Early colonists regarded kangaroos as pests or game animals suitable for sport, giving no thought to conservation.

THE ARRIVAL OF THE FIRST AUSTRALIANS

We know relatively little about the arrival of early humans in Australia — there is still much conjecture as to when the first humans arrived and where they came from. It is now generally accepted though that the first Australians arrived at least 40 000 years and possibly 60 000 years ago, and that they probably travelled from South-East Asia.

At that time sea travel would have been precarious and early vessels would have been simple canoes or rafts. Imagine the new arrivals' surprise and apprehension at discovering the assemblage of unique Pleistocene megafauna — including giant kangaroos, marsupial rhinoceros, giant goannas and marsupial lions — roaming the new land! The arrival of the first Australians was probably the major cause of the mass extinctions of the megafauna, although this is still not fully understood. Humans may have concentrated their hunting skills on the larger species (which provided more meat) and

the less agile or fleet of foot. Also, by practising the technique of firestick farming or burning the bush, they would have altered the pattern of natural fires by increasing their frequency and modifying existing habitats. It is said that today's Red and grey kangaroos are faster than the giant kangaroos, so they were able to survive.

Sadly, over much of present-day Australia, the traditional Aboriginal way of life has long since vanished, much like the giant kangaroos. Kangaroos do, however, remain deeply embedded within the folklore and art of modern Aboriginal people and this relationship stems mainly from their role as a primary food source. Kangaroos also provided leather for clothing and water carriers, their bones were used for spear tips and sinews for twine. Even today traditional kangaroo meat is a highly valued food resource which is hunted, albeit with rifle and dogs, by those Aboriginal people who continue to live something of a traditional lifestyle.

EUROPEAN ENCOUNTERS WITH KANGAROOS

It is now well known that the first European encounter with a kangaroo was made by early explorers, probably Dutch mariners, on the coast of Western Australia. In 1629 Francisco Pelsaert was rescuing survivors from the wreck of the *Batavia* (close to the site of present-day Geraldton), when he reported seeing a small creature which was probably a Tammar Wallaby.

The first written record of a large kangaroo is now accepted as that made by mariners sailing on the *Endeavour* under Captain Cook in 1770. Joseph Banks reported that the animal was 'different from any animal I have seen or read of … It may however be easily known from all other animals by the singular property of running or rather hopping upon its hinderlegs.' In the same year Captain Cook caught an animal near Cooktown which he called 'kangaroo', a word given to him by the local Aboriginal people. Its original meaning has been lost over time and it may be that the natives had misunderstood Cook's questioning; even so, 'kangaroo' has now become probably the most used Aboriginal word in the English language.

THE IMPACT OF EUROPEAN SETTLEMENT

Early this century the spread of agriculture and the intense interest of the early settlers in kangaroos for sport, meat, skins or as vermin to be shot (they were thought to compete with sheep for pasture), brought about massive and tragic reductions of many species. This persecution, together with gross overstocking of sheep in particular, caused severe environmental degradation. The effects of drastic changes to natural habitats has caused the extinction of at least 17 mammal species within Australia during the last 200 years, out of around 36 worldwide. The Riverina area between the Murray and the Murrumbidgee rivers held about 50 species of marsupial at the time of European settlement. Today, only three or four species remain.

THE IMPACT OF INTRODUCED ANIMALS

Introduced rabbits, foxes and feral cats compounded these problems and resulted in the decimation of many of the smaller macropod species, such as Burrowing Bettongs, *Bettongia lesueur*; Bridled Nailtail Wallabies, *Onychogalea fraenata*; and Rufous Hare-wallabies, *Lagorchestes hirsutus*. Rock-wallabies in particular are highly vulnerable to competition with goats and predation by foxes. Brush-tailed Rock-wallabies, *Petrogale penicillata*, were once common in many areas of Victoria but have now all but vanished mainly due to foxes. In addition, between 1884 and 1914, bounties were paid on over 500 000 Brush-tailed Rock-wallabies killed for the fur trade in New South Wales alone.

THE SURVIVORS

A few species of kangaroo have benefited from land clearing and the provision of dams and waterholes. Eastern Grey Kangaroos, Red Kangaroos, and perhaps the Bennett's Wallaby in Tasmania have all increased their populations so that in some areas they are now abundant.

This increase in population of some species has resulted in calls by sections of the community for culling of these so-called pests. Farmers and graziers have frequently attempted to eradicate these species believing them to be competing with their sheep for grass. Recent research into kangaroo biology at Fowlers Gap Research Station has shed light on the issue. It is now believed to be quite possible for kangaroos and sheep to co-exist and the recent studies have shown that there is negligible competition between them for most of the year. It is only during periods of drought that competition can become serious, something which may at times be detrimental to the sheep.

A THRIVING ECONOMY

In many outback areas kangaroos do significantly contribute to the local economy. The harvesting of kangaroos (mainly Red Kangaroos) employs several hundred shooters and the skins are highly valued — they provide a high-quality, light and strong leather with many uses. The meat has long been used for pet food and recently the social stigma of using kangaroo meat for human consumption appears to have waned. Kangaroo meat may now be bought legally at a number of retail outlets and is included on the menu in many fashionable restaurants.

IMPORTANCE TO TOURISM

Both locals and overseas tourists are fascinated by these unusual creatures and for many it is their first choice among things to see when visiting Australia. Many visitors do wish to see kangaroos in the wild and visit outback national parks to enjoy the scenery and unique wildlife. This new concept of ecotourism, when based on sound scientific management techniques, can be an extremely effective tool for conserving wild areas and their flora and fauna. It is important to involve local people, as the more they benefit from nature-based tourism, the more they will work to preserve natural habitats and wildlife.

IN THEIR NATURAL HABITAT

In my travels I frequently meet visitors who ask, 'where can we see kangaroos in the wild?' There are a few areas close to capital cities: Western Grey Kangaroos can be seen on most golf courses close to Perth, Western Australia, while Eastern Grey Kangaroos are common at Tidbinbilla Reserve, Canberra and also at Warrandyte Common, near Melbourne. If visitors are willing to travel further afield there are many superb national parks, reserves and World Heritage areas where a wide range of kangaroos and wallabies may be easily seen or photographed in natural surroundings.

Within New South Wales, the Warrumbungle National Park is a huge area covering a range of forested hills. The more open, low-lying areas hold large populations of Eastern Grey Kangaroos as well as Common Wallaroos and Red-necked

RIGHT The Eastern Grey Kangaroo is known for its excellent hearing. These macropods are able to move their ears independently in order to 'tune in' to a particular sound.

Wallabies, which are all well accustomed to humans. In Kinchega National Park in the far west, the large and beautiful Menindee Lakes, surrounded by arid undulating bluebush plains, are the haunt of Western Grey Kangaroos and Red Kangaroos. Sturt National Park is one of New South Wales' largest conservation areas, covering over 310 000 hectares of semi-arid plains and mesas in the far north-west. The vast gibber plains there are a haven for large numbers of Red Kangaroos.

Victoria has an excellent system of protected areas, including the popular Wilsons Promontory National Park in south Gippsland which is home to a large population of Eastern Grey Kangaroos. The mallee country in north-western Victoria has a wealth of protected areas such as Wyperfeld National Park and Pink Lakes National Park — these support large numbers of Western Grey Kangaroos. Red Kangaroos can be seen at Pink Lakes and Hattah Lakes national parks.

Kangaroo Island off the coast of South Australia is the haunt of the Black-faced Kangaroo, *Macropus fuliginosus fuliginosus*, a subspecies of the Western Grey Kangaroo and the Tammar Wallaby, both of which may be seen in Flinders Chase National Park.

Protecting our Natural Heritage

A zoologist, Dr John Wamsley, has initiated a chain of protected reserves and sanctuaries, mainly within South Australia. At Yookamurra Sanctuary, 125 kilometres from Adelaide, visitors can see Red Kangaroos and Western Greys as well as recently introduced and thriving populations of Burrowing Bettongs and Brush-tailed Bettongs. Facilities are also being developed at newly acquired reserves in the Flinders Ranges, which are the haunt of important colonies of Yellow-footed Rock-wallabies. Rottnest Island near Perth, Western Australia, is one of the country's few strongholds for the Quokka.

Kakadu National Park in the Northern Territory contains many sites where visitors can watch Agile Wallabies and it is possible to view the wary Black Wallaroo, *Macropus bernardus*, at some of the sandstone rock areas such as Nourlangie.

OPPOSITE When first emerging from the pouch, a joey Western Grey Kangaroo spends a considerable amount of time scratching and grooming.
RIGHT Originally widespread and abundant, the Brush-tailed Rock-wallaby has declined severely, particularly in Victoria.

Queensland boasts more species of kangaroo than any other state, including the beautiful Whiptail, or Pretty-face Wallaby, *Macropus parryi*, which is common near camping grounds at Carnarvon National Park in central Queensland. Musky Rat-kangaroos are easily seen scurrying through the leaf litter of the rainforest at Palmerston National Park, south of Cairns.

Tasmania retains a wealth of macropods including some smaller species which, although gone from the mainland, remain widespread due to the lack of foxes and retention of large areas of suitable habitat. The Forester Kangaroo, *Macropus giganteus* (a subspecies of the Eastern Grey Kangaroo), may be seen at Maria Island National Park, Mount William National Park and Asbestos Range National Park. These parks are also home to large numbers of Bennett's Wallaby (the local subspecies of the Red-necked Wallaby) and Tasmanian Pademelon.

The Future

There is nothing, except lack of will, to prevent Australians from living in harmony with kangaroos and other inhabitants of the natural world. Recent conservation programs have amply demonstrated that even the rarest of kangaroo species can be conserved if enough people care and make the effort. Sufficient wild areas must be retained to support adequate populations of macropods. The health of these ecosystems is in our hands; it is important that these habitats and the wealth of kangaroos that live there be preserved for the future.

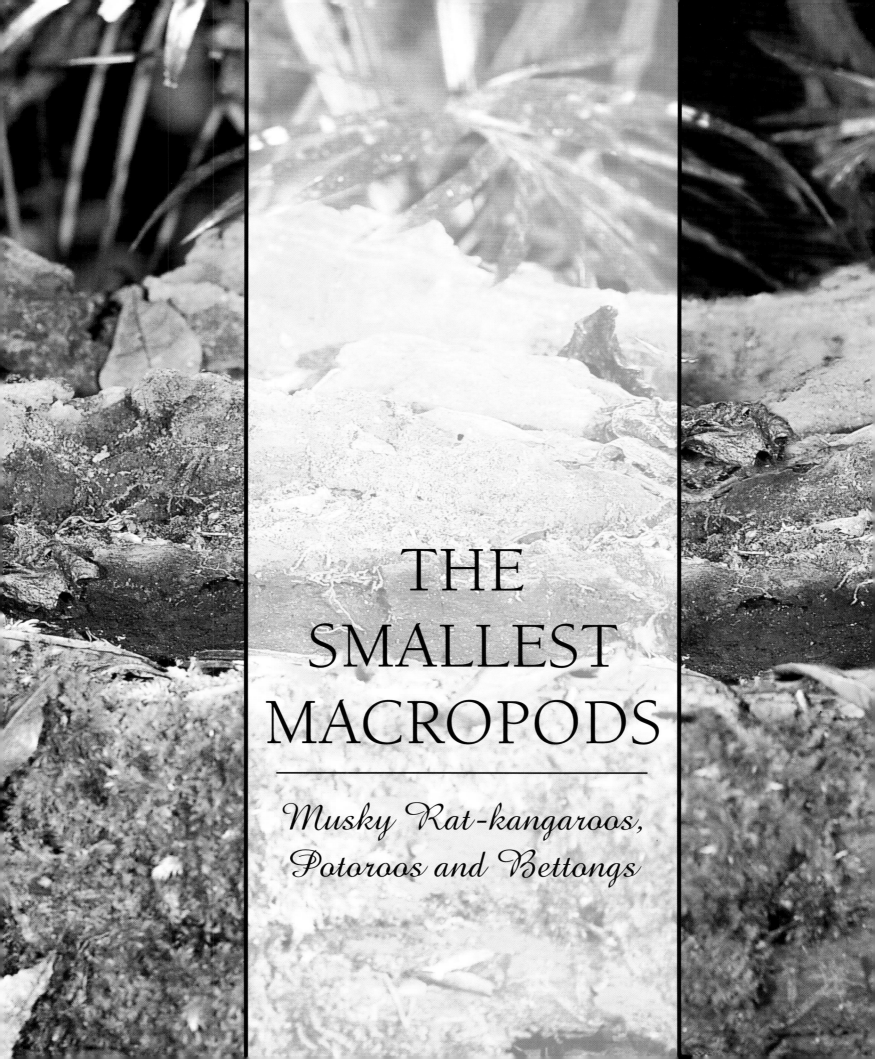

THE SMALLEST MACROPODS

Musky Rat-kangaroos, Potoroos and Bettongs

MUSKY RAT-KANGAROOS, POTOROOS AND BETTONGS

otoroids, the smallest of all kangaroos, are repre-sented by nine known species at present. The smallest of these (weighing approximately 500 grams) is the somewhat bizarre Musky Rat-kangaroo, *Hypsiprymnodon moschatus*, which in many respects is more akin to the possums than to other macropods.

The Musky Rat-kangaroo is a rainforest species, confined to the wet tropics of northern Queensland, where it occurs from sea level to altitudes of about 1200 metres. The brown colour-ing of this most primitive of all kangaroos enables it to blend in with the leaf litter and dark soil of the rainforest floor. The nest is a football-sized structure made of fallen leaves, which is secreted between the buttresses of large trees or among dense vines and roots on the forest floor.

While feeding, these diminutive macropods may drop some seeds of fruit and bury other uneaten food, which aids in the dispersal and regeneration of many trees and thus contributes to the overall health of the ecosystem. Much of the fruit eaten is too toxic to be consumed by other rainforest inhabitants. While feeding, they will not tolerate the presence of other animals, vigorously chasing them from the feeding area. They constantly sniff the air, using their highly developed sense of smell to locate food.

The sexes are surprisingly similar although males are slightly larger. There is a distinct breeding season from February to July; the young remain in the pouch for approximately 21 weeks, after which they follow the mother at foot while foraging.

Musky Rat-kangaroos are easily observed near picnic areas and camping grounds in the lowland rainforest near Mission Beach and at Lake Eacham on the Atherton Tablelands.

Although the population has declined, mainly due to clearing of rainforest for agriculture, the species remains common in large areas of intact rainforest, much of which is now protected by national park and world heritage status.

By contrast, bettongs and potoroos have had a difficult time since European settlement, with most species experiencing severe range reductions and two species becoming extinct — namely the Desert Rat-kangaroo, *Caloprymnus campestris*, and the Broad-faced Potoroo, *Potorous platyops*.

Bettongs and potoroos are smaller than other macropods and have relatively shorter hindfeet. Their diet consists largely of underground fungi, which are dug up with the strongly clawed forefeet, along with some seeds, bulbs and roots. Grasses and insects are sometimes eaten and in Tasmania I have watched entranced as wild Tasmanian Bettongs waited under an exterior light, jumping and catching with great agility the moths attracted to it during warm summer evenings.

Bettongs and potoroos are mainly nocturnal and sleep dur-ing the day in nests built from grasses and other vegetation; these are often hidden in a shallow depression against grass clumps or logs. Bettongs share with the Musky Rat-kangaroo the ability to carry nest material with their prehensile tail.

Although its range has been severely diminished, the Rufous Bettong, *Aepyprymnus rufescens*, is still widely distributed along the east coast of mainland Australia. It prefers forest and wood-land with a sparse grassy understorey.

The Tasmanian Bettong, *Bettongia gaimardi*, was once wide-spread on the south-east mainland of Australia but is now restricted to Tasmania where it remains common in grassy woodlands of the eastern and central districts. I once had the

PREVIOUS PAGES The primitive Musky Rat-kangaroo retains many features of the early proto-kangaroos.
OPPOSITE The Long-footed Potoroo was first discovered in 1978 in far eastern Victoria.

ABOVE The Boodie, or Burrowing Bettong, is the only macropod to regularly live in burrows. These are frequently complex systems with several entrances and housing many individuals. OPPOSITE   The Musky Rat-kangaroo remains common in the rainforests of north-eastern Queensland and is frequently seen near picnic areas and camping grounds.

privilege of rehabilitating an orphaned Tasmanian Bettong and used to follow it through the bush, watching as it sniffed the ground before digging furiously and unearthing small round fungi the size of walnuts.

Burrowing Bettongs, or Boodies, *Bettongia lesueur*, had been wiped out on the Australian mainland and were only found on Bernier and Dorre islands in Shark Bay, and Boodie and Barrow islands off the coast of the Pilbara, in Western Australia. In recent years, Boodies have been reintroduced into several large reserves which have been fenced to exclude predators.

Potoroos consist of four species of which two species, the Broad-faced Potoroo, *Potorous platyops*, and Gilbert's Potoroo, *Potorous gilbertii*, from Western Australia, were until recently considered extinct. During November 1994, two researchers were setting traps at Two Peoples Bay Reserve, on the south coast of Western Australia, in the hope of catching Quokkas. They were mystified when an animal resembling a small wallaby was caught, followed by two more the next day. Gilbert's Potoroo had not been recorded officially since 1879 but the researchers soon realised that the mystery animal fitted the description given by John Gould over a century ago. Following exhaustive tests and measurements by staff from the Western Australian Museum, it was finally declared that the Gilbert's Potoroo had been rediscovered alive and well!

The Long-footed Potoroo, *Potorous longipes*, was first discovered in 1978 in the wet forests of East Gippsland, Victoria, where it inhabits areas with a dense understorey of sedges, ferns and shrubs. The known distribution of this species is small, covering only about 80 square kilometres, and the population remains rare and endangered. A captive colony has, however, been established at Healesville Sanctuary, near Melbourne, where it is reproducing successfully.

The Long-nosed Potoroo, *Potorous tridactylus*, remains fairly widespread in south-eastern Australia and is common in Tasmania. Although mainly nocturnal, the Long-nosed Potoroo is sometimes active during the day, but it prefers areas with dense ground cover. There the potoroos form a network of runways and tunnels from which they rarely depart.

RELICS FROM GONDWANA

It is now widely accepted that all macropods evolved from possum-like animals which lived in the forests of Gondwana around 150 million years ago. For these leaf-chomping, tree-dwelling marsupials life would have been easy. Even so, some of them — perhaps in search of fallen fruit, blossom or leaves — did descend to ground level and remained there. Adapting to a life on the ground floor caused many species to radically evolve and adapt their shape and lifestyle to suit the new conditions.

The Musky Rat-kangaroo which is still common in rainforests of the wet tropics is the one species to retain several of these early possum characteristics. It is the only macropod species to have five toes on the hindfoot including an opposable toe which possums use for climbing. Possums are adept at using their prehensile tails while climbing and the Musky Rat-kangaroo has also retained the ability to clasp with its tail as it clambers over fallen trees on the forest floor.

Unlike other macropods, the Musky Rat-kangaroo has never evolved the ability to hop, instead it bounds on all fours similar to possums. It is also the only macropod to regularly produce twins or even triplets, once again similar to some possums. This smallest of all macropods is also unique in being largely diurnal, foraging for fruit, seeds and fungi during the day.

RIGHT A generally solitary creature, the Musky Rat-kangaroo does sometimes gather in small groups to feed on fallen fruit on the rainforest floor. This often erupts into noisy squabbling with animals chasing each other over possession of food.

ABOVE An inhabitant of coastal heathland and forests with a dense understorey, the Long-nosed Potoroo can sometimes be seen foraging during daylight hours.

BELOW The Long-footed Potoroo feeds largely on the fruiting organisms of underground fungi and is thought to aid in the dispersal of these important plants.

OPPOSITE The search is now on for more populations of the recently rediscoverd Gilbert's Potoroo which, at present, has only been recorded at Two Peoples Bay, Western Australia.

BELOW Gilbert's Potoroo has small front feet which are armed with powerful claws used for digging. The short ears are almost hidden in the animal's long fur.

ABOVE The diet of the Brush-tailed Bettong consists largely of fungi, bulbs, seeds, tubers and insects.

LEFT Brush-tailed Bettongs sleep in nests made of grass and shredded bark, constructed over shallow depressions.

OPPOSITE BOTTOM LEFT Similar to other species of bettong, the Brush-tailed Bettong has a prehensile tail which it can use to carry nest material.

OPPOSITE BOTTOM RIGHT Rufous Bettongs are widely distributed in open grassy woodlands of Western Australia.

OPPOSITE TOP The Rufous Bettong is the largest of all bettong species and, like most, is nocturnal.

RIGHT Tasmanian Bettongs are widely distributed in eastern Tasmania due to the suitable habitat and an absence of predation by foxes.

BELOW   The Burrowing Bettong has recently been successfully re-introduced into fenced, predator-free reserves in South Australia.

COMPACT
& UNIQUE

Tree-kangaroos and
Pademelons

TREE-KANGAROOS AND PADEMELONS

Kangaroos never fail to amaze me with their ability to live in and adapt to an incredibly broad range of landforms and habitats — something clearly demonstrated by tree-kangaroos. Although often regarded as oddities, the approximately 10 species of tree-kangaroo represent about one-sixth of all living kangaroos. Eight of these are found in New Guinea and the remaining two in northern Queensland.

Tree-kangaroos evolved from rock-wallabies over five million years ago. Rock-wallabies demonstrate similar movements and sometimes clamber among the lower branches of trees. In New South Wales, fossils have been found of a giant tree-kangaroo which lived at least 50 000 years ago. This extraordinary animal would have been similar in size to a present-day mature Red Kangaroo. It is not clear why tree-kangaroos have forsaken their formerly terrestrial lifestyle and returned to an arboreal existence, but it may have been triggered by the existence of large areas of rainforest which constituted an unutilised or vacant niche with an abundant food source.

While tree-kangaroos spend most of their time clambering or hopping high in trees, they do at times come down to the ground where they are able to hop rapidly. When descending trees they usually slide or walk down backwards, although they have been recorded jumping from a height of up to 20 metres above the ground without injury. Not particularly energetic animals, they spend most of the day asleep or resting on a branch. This may, in part, be due to their diet of leaves which would be unlikely to support an active lifestyle.

Lumholtz's Tree-kangaroo, *Dendrolagus lumholtzi*, is the smallest of all tree-kangaroos and is found in high-elevation (over 800 metres) tropical rainforests of northern Queensland. This limited distribution includes the Atherton Tablelands where much of its habitat has unfortunately been cleared. Tree-kangaroos are notoriously difficult to see in the wild due to their secretive and nocturnal habits; however, their pale cream belly combined with the habit of preferring forest edges make the generally solitary Lumholtz's Tree-kangaroos easier to locate than the second Australian species, Bennett's Tree-kangaroo, *Dendrolagus bennettianus*.

Bennett's Tree-kangaroo only occurs in a small area, about 75 kilometres by 50 kilometres, north of the Daintree River. Its diet consists largely of leaves supplemented with epiphytes such as Staghorn Ferns, and some fruit.

The closely related pademelons are small, stocky macropods with relatively short tails. They feed on grasses and low shrubs in forests with a dense understorey. Like Musky Rat-kangaroos, pademelons use all four legs when moving at a slow pace. However, as with other kangaroos, they hop on their hind legs when moving quickly.

The Red-legged Pademelon, *Thylogale stigmatica*, is found in the rainforest and wet sclerophyll forest of eastern Australia from Cape York to the mid-New South Wales coast. Unusually, this secretive species will feed on dead leaves, many of which are quite dry and crunchy, picked up from the forest floor. Other favoured food includes fruits such as figs and Burdekin plums. In common with the other pademelons this species thumps the ground with its hindfeet as an alarm signal. The Red-legged and Red-necked pademelons are preyed upon by dingoes, Spotted-tailed Quolls, Amethystine Pythons, and foxes.

PREVIOUS PAGES   Frequenting forest edges, the Red-necked Pademelon is a timid creature that sometimes feeds in groups.
OPPOSITE   The nocturnal Lumholtz's Tree-kangaroo feeds on a range of leaves and plants in tropical rainforests.

ADAPTATIONS FOR TREE-TOP LIVING

It now appears that some kangaroos — having evolved from possum-like ancestors and being at home living on the ground — did return to an arboreal lifestyle. The reasons for this are not entirely clear, but perhaps they recognised an ample source of food high in the trees, a vacant niche secure from large predators.

The strange decision for these originally ground-dwelling animals to re-adapt to living high in trees does seem to have been successful, as they have co-existed with other macropods for over five million years.

To help them grasp branches while climbing, tree-kangaroos have evolved proportionally stronger and larger forelimbs. The hindfeet are shorter and broader than ground-dwelling kangaroos enabling them to better grip the surface of branches. Their ankles and wrists are more flexible, allowing a certain amount of sideways movement and they are able to walk, unlike most other kangaroos which can only hop. They also have long curved claws which increase their grip, while their long tail is very useful as a balance, particularly when leaping from branch to branch.

A large stomach is required for digesting a diet of leaves, many of which are toxic to other animals, and tree-kangaroos make use of shearing teeth rather than the grinding teeth of other macropods.

Lumholtz's Tree Kangaroo, depicted above, spends most of its life high in the rainforest canopy. Here it is safe from harm as long as its habitat is protected.

The Red-necked Pademelon, *Thylogale thetis*, is a common inhabitant of the rainforest and wet sclerophyll forest of eastern New South Wales and south-eastern Queensland, where it prefers forest edges. The reddish-brown fur around the neck of this species readily distinguishes it from the Red-legged Pademelon with which its range overlaps. Red-necked Pademelons may be active at times during the day and in winter will bask in the sun in small open areas. Towards dusk animals move from the forest cover to more open areas to graze but, being timid creatures, they rarely venture far from the forest edge. At Lamington National Park in south-eastern Queensland, they are commonly seen grazing near the camping ground and parking areas.

The Tasmanian Pademelon, *Thylogale billardierii*, formerly occurred in Victoria and south-eastern South Australia, but is now restricted to Australia's island state where it remains wide-spread. This wallaby is also found on several Bass Strait islands including Flinders, Cape Barren, King and the Hunter Group.

The species was formerly called the Red-bellied Pademelon, or Rufous Wallaby, due to the rufous-buff colour of the fur on the lower abdomen. Males are noticeably larger and have more muscular forearms and chests than females. Top-ranking males establish dominance hierarchies through ritualised aggression in order to obtain exlusive mating rights with several females. Breeding is continuous throughout the year, although most young are born in early winter. Following its departure from the pouch after approximately six months, the joey grows rapidly, and is at first frequently left under a bush or other secure place while the mother ventures out into the open to feed.

At certain national parks, such as Asbestos Range and Mount William in Tasmania's north, large numbers of these pade-melons may be seen feeding at dusk on cleared areas adjacent to forests. Tasmanian Pademelons show a fondness for blossom and I have frequently watched them feeding on the flowers of Common Heath, *Epacris impressa*.

These intriguing wallabies have adapted to a broad range of habitats ranging from coastal heathland and sclerophyll forest to high alpine country where deep snow falls are frequent. Here Tasmanian Pademelons are adept at digging with their forepaws to uncover buried vegetation.

OPPOSITE The Tasmanian Pademelon is able to breed all year round, although most young are born in early winter.

ABOVE   Bennett's Tree Kangaroo is a rarely seen macropod from north-eastern Queensland.

RIGHT   Lumholtz's Tree-kangaroo is not particularly energetic and spends most of the day resting out of sight of the ground on a high branch. A large stomach is required to digest the leafy diet.

ABOVE The Red-legged Pademelon, which also occurs in New Guinea, prefers rainforests where it is able to eat dead leaves.

OPPOSITE The Tasmanian Pademelon is extremely adept at using its forepaws to pull down the blossoms of shrubs.

BELOW Male Tasmanian Pademelons often behave aggressively and will frequently engage in bouts of boxing.

RIGHT AND FOLLOWING PAGES Sometimes in daylight hours, small groups of Red-necked Pademelons may be seen feeding in small clearings or on grassy areas adjacent to forests.

GRACE & STYLE

Large Kangaroos and Wallabies

LARGE KANGAROOS AND WALLABIES

*L*arge kangaroos add a powerful presence to a natural landscape and are immediately recognisable icons of the animal world. The genus *Macropus* includes all the large species of kangaroo and many wallabies ranging from the large Red-necked Wallaby, *Macropus rufogriseus*, to the small Tammar Wallaby, *Macropus eugenii*.

Possibly the most handsome of all kangaroos, the Red Kangaroo, *Macropus rufus*, weighs up to 85 kilograms and is the largest native land vertebrate found in Australia. This species is characteristic of semi-arid inland Australia and is widely distributed throughout salt plains, mulga and mallee scrub, deserts and grassland. It is, however, dependent on water and green herbage which affects both the number of females breeding and the number of young joeys that survive. The large numbers of Red Kangaroos south and east of the dingo fence in west Queensland are due to the proliferation of artificial dams and waterholes as well as to the eradication of the dingo as a predator.

The provision of additional dispersed watering points for sheep and cattle has benefited other large macropods, including the Eastern Grey Kangaroo, *Macropus giganteus*, and the Western Grey Kangaroo, *Macropus fuliginosus*. These are the large kangaroos most commonly seen in Australia, particularly in national parks and reserves where large mobs may be encountered feeding in the late afternoon. Colonial feeding has its advantages, particularly on the open plains where the many ears and eyes make it extremely difficult for a predator to approach unnoticed.

The Common Wallaroo, or Euro, *Macropus robustus*, is a robust kangaroo with a characteristic upright bounding gait. It prefers the rocky hills and gorges of the arid inland as well as more fertile areas of the east. Wallaroos rest during the day under rocks or in caves in order to escape the intense sun, venturing out late in the day to feed on slopes lower down.

The shy and rarely seen Black Wallaroo, *Macropus bernardus*, has a range limited to steep rocky escarpments of Arnhem Land in the Northern Territory. A few of these animals have become accustomed to people in Kakadu National Park where they may be seen near rock-art sites such as Nourlangie.

The Antilopine Wallaroo, *Macropus antilopinus*, is a large tropical macropod which fills a similar ecological niche to the Eastern and Western Grey Kangaroos of Australia's southern regions. It is also sometimes referred to as the Antilopine Kangaroo as it is similar to red and grey kangaroos in behaviour, habitat and appearance. Antilopine Wallaroos are gregarious, occurring in groups of up to 30, although solitary animals are frequently seen.

The Red-necked Wallaby, *Macropus rufogriseus*, is the large wallaby most often seen in forests and scrub of south-east Australia and Tasmania. Red-necked Wallabies from Tasmania — correctly known as Bennett's Wallabies — differ considerably from their mainland counterparts and have longer and denser fur. Most females give birth in late summer and the joey remains in the pouch for nine months. As with other macropods they are prolific breeders when conditions are ideal. I recently observed a juvenile we named Rusty that had left her mother's pouch a year earlier. Rusty was still suckling from her mother, despite already having a joey of her own at foot!

The Tammar Wallaby, *Macropus eugenii*, has a similar breeding pattern to Bennett's Wallaby and is one of the smallest *Macropus*

PREVIOUS PAGES Male Forester Kangaroos frequently engage in bouts of boxing, especially during spring.
OPPOSITE Although now independent, this juvenile Bennett's Wallaby still maintains a strong bond with its mother.

wallabies. Populations are scattered on several offshore islands as well as in some areas of mainland Western Australia and South Australia. Fresh water is often not available for several months on some of the semi-arid islands and the species has evolved the ability to drink sea water when necessary. Interestingly, Tammar Wallbies are being used as surrogate mothers to foster young Brush-tailed Rock-wallabies, *Petrogale penicillata*, in an attempt to bolster populations of this declining species.

The Parma Wallaby, *Macropus parma*, is similar in size to the Tammar and inhabits forests of eastern New South Wales with a dense understorey. Cryptic and retiring by nature, it was until recently considered extinct. During the 1960s Parma Wallabies were discovered on Kawau Island, New Zealand, where they had been introduced by settlers over 100 years earlier. Some of these were saved from shooting (they had become pests) and sent to Australia for captive breeding purposes; however, soon afterwards surveys discovered natural populations alive and well, and possibly even increasing, in north-eastern New South Wales.

The Black-striped Wallaby, *Macropus dorsalis*, is a social species which remains common in many areas of east Australia, particularly Queensland. As it prefers scrub and forest environments with a dense understorey, this large wallaby is rarely seen and has been, as a result, little studied.

In contrast, the Agile Wallaby, *Macropus agilis*, a common macropod of tropical coastal Australia, is very visible in many areas of Queensland such as Cape Hillsborough and Bowling Green Bay national parks, and Kakadu National Park in the Northern Territory. An alert and nervous animal, the Agile Wallaby frequently thumps the ground to warn of danger. It is a gregarious animal and mobs of up to 20 or more may be seen grazing in the early morning or late afternoon.

The Western Brush Wallaby, *Macropus irma*, remains common in the dry forests and woodland (particularly jarrah) of south-west Western Australia. It is more diurnal than many other macropods, and has a particularly long tail in comparison to its relatively small body. A recent decline in numbers has been attributed to the large increase in fox numbers — these animals prey on the juvenile wallabies as soon as they leave the pouch.

RIGHT Common Wallaroos emerge in late afternoon from their daytime rest areas among rocks to feed on grasses and shrubs lower down on the slopes.

WHY DO KANGAROOS LICK THEIR FOREARMS?

Vast tracts of Australia consist of semi-arid plains and scrub which, during summer months, bake in the intense glare and heat. Many species of kangaroo inhabiting these hot lands have, however, evolved a variety of strategies for dealing with the climate.

Most macropods rest in the shade of a bush or tree during daylight hours, when solar radiation is most intense. This resting conserves energy and water which is a scarce and precious resource. It would be most dangerous to indulge in high physical activity when daytime air temperatures exceed 40°C.

Another useful strategy frequently seen in the larger kangaroos is forearm licking, as demonstrated above by a juvenile Eastern Grey Kangaroo. A maze of blood vessels is situated close to the surface of the skin of the forearms and during hot weather the kangaroo frequently licks its forearms, depositing saliva on the thin covering of fur in this area. Heat is lost from the body as the saliva evaporates. This cools the skin and the blood vessels close to the surface. Cool venous blood, returning to the heart, assists in lowering the kangaroo's body temperature. However, forearm licking does use up valuable water and so needs to be performed sparingly particularly in drought conditions. Panting is the major method used by kangaroos to lose heat.

ABOVE Male Red Kangaroos can grow to twice the bulk of females, with a broad chest and powerful muscular forearms. BELOW Female Red Kangaroos are usually a soft blue-grey colour, although a few do have reddish coats. Red Kangaroos are essentially grazing animals that are capable of surviving without water if the herbage is green.

ABOVE Shortly after the breaking of a drought, female Red Kangaroos are able to regain full breeding potential. The joey vacates the pouch after eight months and continues to suckle while running at foot for another three months.

BELOW LEFT The proliferation of artificial waterholes has led to an increase in Red Kangaroos in some areas.

BELOW RIGHT A Red Kangaroo seen bounding at speed across a plain epitomises outback Australia.

LEFT This adult male Red Kangaroo was photographed as it approached a rapidly drying waterhole during late afternoon. Red Kangaroos may be observed easily from a vehicle in several outback national parks.

TOP AND ABOVE Sub-adult male Eastern Grey Kangaroos frequently engage in 'play' boxing. Note how the powerful tail is used by each kangaroo as a support.

LEFT This adult male Eastern Grey Kangaroo is unruffled by the photographer as he scratches.

OPPOSITE TOP During 'play' boxing — which may continue for some time — these sub-adult male Eastern Grey Kangaroos are unlikely to suffer serious injury.

OPPOSITE BOTTOM Bounding elegantly across a plain in northern Tasmania, this male Forester Kangaroo demonstrates how evolution has produced a highly efficient means of locomotion.

PREVIOUS PAGES Eastern Grey Kangaroos have adapted to a wide variety of habitats including the coastline and venture onto beaches in some areas.

TOP   During courtship a male Eastern Grey Kangaroo follows a female closely, regularly checking to see if she is receptive, prior to mating.

ABOVE   Following courtship, which may last for several days, a male Eastern Grey Kangaroo is able to mate successfully when the female reaches oestrus.

RIGHT   As demonstrated by Eastern Grey Kangaroos, the long and powerful tail is used for balance while bounding.

ABOVE When moving slowly a Western Grey Kangaroo places its forefeet on the ground and then moves the hindfeet forward while using the tail as a support.

LEFT This sub-adult male Western Grey Kangaroo is similar to an Eastern Grey except that the fur is medium to dark chocolate-brown.

OPPOSITE This Western Grey Kangaroo joey has recently left the pouch and will continue to suckle for another nine months.

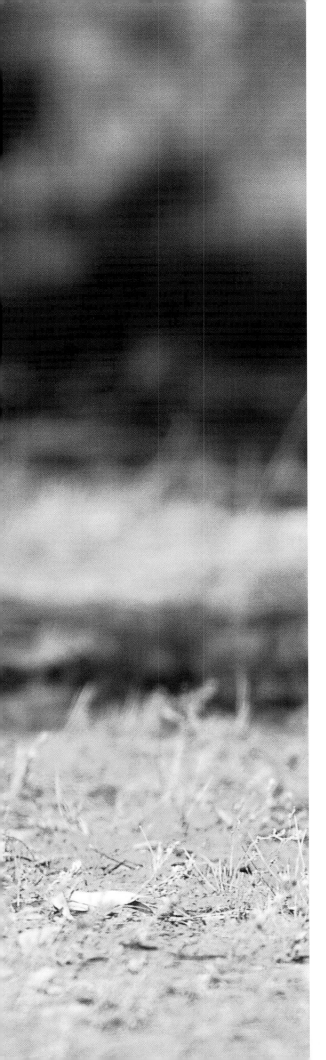

LEFT This Western Grey Kangaroo joey spends time out of the pouch during early morning and will climb back in at any hint of danger.

BELOW After birth, the young Western Grey Kangaroo crawls through the mother's belly fur into the pouch and attaches itself to a nipple. The joey remains in the pouch for about another 10 months.

BOTTOM These adult male Western Grey Kangaroos are bracing for a fight which will establish superiority and thereby allow the dominant male to mate with females in oestrus.

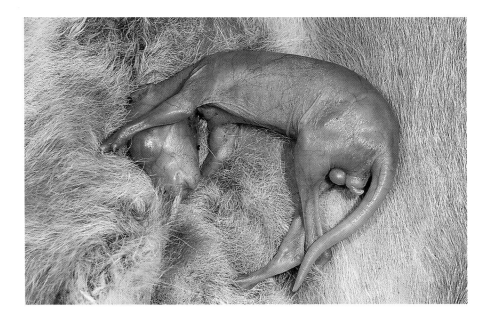

ABOVE   Young kangaroos frequently touch noses briefly with adults as a form of greeting, as demonstrated by these Agile Wallabies.

LEFT A small wallaby which was once thought extinct, the Parma Wallaby remains rare in dense forests of far eastern Australia. Generally solitary, they sometimes gather in small groups to feed.

OPPOSITE A common macropod in Australia's tropical north, the Agile Wallaby is able to breed all year. It is a particularly timid and alert animal.

TOP Prime Whiptail Wallaby habitat, consisting of open forest with a grassy under-storey, is found at Carnarvon National Park, south-east Queensland.

ABOVE Whiptail Wallabies rarely drink except during extreme drought; at other times they are able to obtain enough moisture from their food. This social species lives in groups of up to 50, and is unusual in that it is often active during the day.

RIGHT The Tammar Wallaby is one of the smallest wallabies. Common on some islands off Western Australia and South Australia, it is known to drink sea water.

LEFT The Bennett's Wallaby of Tasmania has a heavier build and longer and denser fur than its mainland counterpart.

BELOW This female Bennett's Wallaby is 'play' fighting with her almost fully grown youngster from the previous year.

OPPOSITE A wary and rarely seen macropod, the solitary Black Wallaroo is restricted to steep, rugged escarpments of a small area of central and western Arnhem Land.

ABOVE The Common Wallaroo, or Euro, is well adapted to semi-arid conditions and is able to survive in areas with little standing water.

RIGHT Common Wallaroos have a distinctive stance and a coarse, shaggy-haired coat. Old males, as depicted here, become darker — almost black — and heavier with age.

OPPOSITE Female Common Wallaroos are considerably smaller than males, with a coarse blue-grey coat. They are able to breed all year round.

AGILE & SOCIABLE

Rock-wallabies

ROCK-WALLABIES

Rock-wallabies, of which there are at least 15 species, are some of Australia's most attractive and fascinating macropods. As their name suggests, they live in rocky areas or gorges where they are able to shelter from the sun and hide from predators. Rock-wallabies are able to move with speed and grace over rocky terrain due to the heavily granulated soles of their feet which provide friction and a secure grip on the slippery surface of rocks. Their tail is used as an aid to balance and is frequently carried arched over the back when hopping at speed.

Most rock-wallabies sleep during the heat of the day under rocks or overhangs or in small caves, emerging to feed on a wide variety of plants during late afternoon and throughout the night. Individuals frequently bask in the sun during early morning, particularly following a cold night.

One of the most beautiful of all macropods is the Yellow-footed Rock-wallaby, *Petrogale xanthopus*, which occurs on rocky ranges and outcrops in semi-arid regions of South Australia, New South Wales and Queensland. This striking animal is the largest of all rock-wallabies and the greyish-buff back contrasts with a rich brown stripe down the back, white along its sides and cheeks, and rufous-brown arms and legs. The long tail is handsomely marked with yellow and brown bands.

During early summer of last year I was sitting by a small creek which wound along a jagged gorge in the Gammon Ranges of South Australia. I was alerted by a small movement upstream and, through my binoculars, could just make out a female Yellow-footed Rock-wallaby which had come down to drink. I watched enthralled as she delicately picked up stones from the rapidly drying creek bed and licked the wet mossy undersides.

Unfortunately, as with most other species of rock-wallaby, the Yellow-footed suffered a severe decline with European settlement and was hunted excessively for skins. Although now fully protected, surviving colonies have to compete for food with large numbers of feral goats, rabbits and farm stock. Predation by foxes and feral cats is also severe; however, many colonies are now protected within national parks and reserves where these introduced pest species are controlled.

The smallest of all rock-wallabies, the Warabi, *Petrogale burbidgei*, was only recently discovered living in the remote and rugged sandstone country of the Kimberleys, in Western Australia. The Warabi is easily confused with the Nabarlek or Little Rock-wallaby, *Petrogale concinna*, although the species do prefer different habitats — Nabarleks also have a greater distribution, including parts of Kakadu National Park and Arnhem Land, Northern Territory.

One of the most widespread of all rock-wallabies is the Black-footed Rock-wallaby, *Petrogale lateralis*, which occurs in widely scattered colonies across Western Australia, the Northern Territory, Queensland and South Australia. This species is also suffering a severe and continuing decline in numbers largely due to predation by foxes.

The Purple-necked Rock-wallaby, *Petrogale lateralis purpureicollis*, was originally considered a sub-species of the Black-footed, but recent research indicates it is a separate species.

Several species of rock-wallaby are found in Queensland including the Mareeba Rock-wallaby, *Petrogale mareeba*. As with some other species, this small rock-wallaby lacks any distinctive markings and varies in colour from light brown to almost black, depending on the colour of the rocks where it lives.

PREVIOUS PAGES The Black-footed Rock-wallaby inhabits rocky ranges of central and western Australia.
OPPOSITE Although largely nocturnal, the Yellow-footed Rock-wallaby basks in the sun during winter.

The Allied Rock-wallaby, *Petrogale assimilis*, was originally considered the same species as the Mareeba Rock-wallaby. It is now considered a separate species and is widespread in north-eastern Queensland including Bowling Green Bay National Park.

As with most other rock-wallabies, when the Allied young leaves the pouch it is left in a small cave or shelter under a rock while the mother ventures out to feed. This is probably in response to the difficulty a joey would have keeping up with its mother in such rugged terrain.

The Brush-tailed Rock-wallaby, *Petrogale penicillata*, was originally widespread and abundant in Victoria, New South Wales and south-eastern Queensland and occurred in a range of rocky habitats. The severely depleted populations are now the subject of intense management in an attempt to save the species. Critically endangered in Victoria, a small surviving colony has recently been discovered in the Grampians National Park and, using automatic cameras triggered by an infra-red beam, researchers have managed to record individuals on film.

A greatly expanded program of fox control is in progress which should help reduce predation. A captive breeding program is also being undertaken at Healesville Sanctuary, Victoria, with the aim of eventually reintroducing animals back into the wild. Young rock-wallabies are removed from their mother's pouch at an early age in a process of cross-fostering. They are then placed in the pouch of a surrogate mother of another species (Tammar Wallabies and Yellow-footed Rock-wallabies) where they are reared. Female Brush-tailed Rock-wallabies are then able to produce up to seven joeys per year.

OPPOSITE   Lacking any distinct markings, the Allied Rock-wallaby is widespread in north-eastern Queensland including Palm and Magnetic islands.

BELOW   Sheltering in a small cave, this joey Mareeba Rock-wallaby is just beginning to explore the world outside its mother's pouch for the first time.

ABOVE The fur coloration of the Allied Rock-wallaby varies from dark brown to grey-brown depending on the rock type of its habitat.

LEFT The world's smallest rock-wallaby is the Monjon, or Warabi, which was only discoverd recently in the rugged Kimberley region.

OPPOSITE A little known species from the tropical north, the Short-eared Rock-wallaby varies considerably in coloration and size, depending on its habitat and locality.

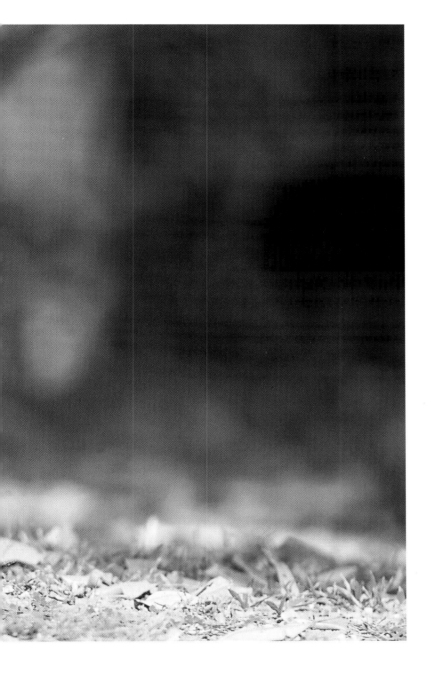

HAVE POUCH WILL TRAVEL

Macropods are not the only animals to rear young in a pouch. Most other marsupials such as quolls, bandicoots, possums and wombats also exhibit this feature.

The female Mareeba Rock-wallaby depicted above has a forward-facing pouch which contains four teats (as do all other macropods), although only one young is usually born at a time. Immediately after giving birth the young macropod (approximately the size of a small pea) clambers through the fur on the mother's belly and into the pouch where it fastens to a nipple. From here growth is rapid until the joey — now with fur — vacates the pouch after about 3.5 months for potoroos, 6.5 months for rock-wallabies and 8 to 10 months for the large kangaroos.

After most macropods have given birth the female immediately becomes sexually receptive. However, as a joey is already suckling in the pouch, the second fertilised ovum ceases development until a few weeks prior to the original joey vacating the pouch. This phenomenon is known as delayed implantation of the embryo. Once the original joey vacates the pouch it continues to suckle 'at foot' for several more weeks. By now the second young has been born and is attached to a second nipple inside the pouch. Remarkably the female is now suckling two joeys at different stages of development and the two mammary glands are able to produce milk of differing composition, tailored to the different needs of the joeys, for each teat.

RIGHT   Mareeba Rock-wallabies are sociable animals occurring as localised colonies of over 100 individuals on rocky outcrops and gorges.

BELOW   During late afternoon, a group of Mareeba Rock-wallabies emerges from its daytime shelter to investigate the photographer's rucksack.

ABOVE   The beautiful Yellow-footed Rock-wallaby has severely declined in numbers since European settlement.

RIGHT   Formerly abundant near the Jenolan Caves, New South Wales, the colony of Brush-tailed Rock-wallabies is now protected by predator-proof fencing.

OPPOSITE   A widespread species, the Black-footed Rock-wallaby is found in central and western Australia.

LEFT These Yellow-footed Rock-wallabies have emerged from their high rocky habitat in the Gammon Ranges, South Australia, where they are easy to observe.

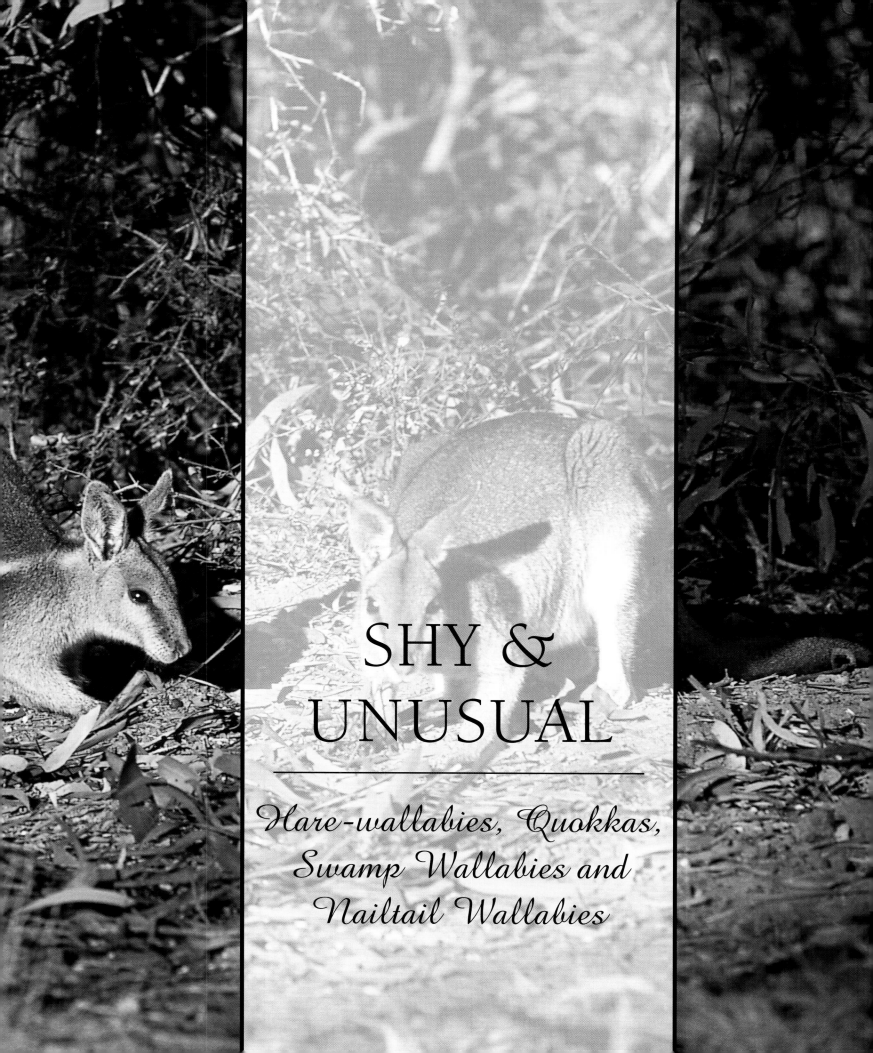

SHY & UNUSUAL

Hare-wallabies, Quokkas, Swamp Wallabies and Nailtail Wallabies

HARE-WALLABIES, QUOKKAS, SWAMP WALLABIES AND NAILTAIL WALLABIES

The huge diversity of macropods has produced many unusual and unique forms which do not fit into any of the normal groups. The Quokka, *Setonix brachyurus*, was one of the first marsupials referred to by early Dutch explorers in 1658. It was later described as being like a big rat and the island of Rottnest, at the mouth of Western Australia's Swan River, which has a thriving population of Quokkas, was first named 'Rottenest' (rat's nest) in honour of this small macropod.

The Quokka resembles other small wallabies although it has a much shorter tail and browses on low shrubs rather than grazing. Only found on the mainland in the wetter parts of south-western Western Australia, it is active mainly at night and prefers swamps, densely vegetated forests and heaths. Although it suffered a severe decline on the mainland during this century, some recovery of numbers has recently taken place.

The Swamp Wallaby, *Wallabia bicolor*, is a large anomalous wallaby which is sufficiently different to other wallabies for it to be classified as the only surviving member of its genus, *Wallabia*. The dark brown coloration and pale muzzle stripe immediately distinguish this macropod from others. With a wide distribution from the tip of Cape York to south-western Victoria, it prefers areas of dense vegetation to rest in during the day and emerges at night to feed in more open areas. It is a shy and wary animal and is only infrequently observed except in some national parks such as Carnarvon National Park in Queensland, where it is tame around the camping ground.

The Swamp Wallaby is primarily a browsing animal and is able to feed on young pine trees and bracken as well as on coarser native shrubs.

The group of wallabies known as nailtail wallabies comprises two species which have suffered severely since the arrival of Europeans in Australia. Another species, the Crescent Nailtail Wallaby, *Onychogalea lunata*, was once widespread across much of arid central and western Australia but is now extinct. Their name comes from the horny 'nail' at the tip of their tail.

The Northern Nailtail Wallaby, *Onychogalea unguifera*, remains common throughout its range and, at present, it appears to be under little threat. The species seems able to tolerate modifications to its habitat from stock grazing.

The Bridled Nailtail Wallaby, *Onychogalea fraenata*, was until recently considered extinct, following a severe decline from its broad band of distribution ranging from northern Queensland to western Victoria. In 1973 a cattleman near Dingo in central Queensland was reading an article about extinct species in a national magazine. Seeing a drawing of the supposedly extinct Bridled Nailtail Wallaby he realised the same animal was alive and well on his property. Following confirmation by zoologists, the 11 400 hectare property was acquired and fully protected as Taunton Scientific Reserve. With the exclusion of stock and control of predators, the population has increased to around 2000. Captive breeding colonies of this still endangered species have now been established at several localitites, including Pallarenda research centre, near Townsville. The species has also been released into the 140 000-hectare Idalia National Park.

Another group of small macropods which has suffered a severe decline since the arrival of Europeans is that of the hare-wallabies. The small Central Hare-wallaby, *Lagorchestes asomatus*, is only known to science from a single specimen

PREVIOUS PAGES The Bridled Nailtail Wallaby is now restricted to two small protected areas of Queensland.
OPPOSITE An inhabitant of forests with dense undergrowth, the Swamp Wallaby is a very wary animal.

collected during 1932 in the west of the Northern Territory. It is now almost certainly extinct.

The Spectacled Hare-wallaby, *Lagorchestes conspicillatus*, has not suffered the same fate and remains widespread across much of tropical Australia where it prefers open forests, woodlands and scrub with a grassy understorey. Spectacled Hare-wallabies prefer areas of dense spinifex grass or hummock grass where they make tunnels to escape the intense daytime temperatures. They are able to breed all year, but can delay embryo development during drought conditions.

The Rufous Hare-wallaby, or Mala, *Lagorchestes hirsutus*, was formerly common across much of central and western Australia where its preferred habitat was spinifex hummock grasslands. It no longer exists in the wild on mainland Australia although it does occur on Bernier and Dorre islands in Shark Bay. A captive colony has been established near Alice Springs with animals trapped in the Tanami Desert and research is continuing into the feasibility of re-introducing the species into the wild. Before this can happen the habitat needs to be made suitable by eradicating predators such as feral cats and foxes. It also appears that the mosaic of vegetation produced by small-scale controlled burning, previously carried out by Aboriginal people, provided the Mala with the diversity of flora it required. A suitable burning regime is now under way with the help of local Aborigines.

The Banded Hare-wallaby, *Lagostrophus fasciatus*, is believed by many zoologists to be the sole surviving member of the sthenurines, a formerly large group of macropods which lived in Australia over two million years ago. It is now only found on Bernier and Dorre islands in Shark Bay. A small nocturnal macropod, it prefers areas of dense acacia thickets and similar shrublands where it shelters from the intense sun, emerging at night to feed on herbs, shrub shoots and grasses.

OPPOSITE The Spectacled Hare-wallaby is widespread across the tropical grasslands and grassy open woodlands of northern Australia. Although it has declined in other regions, it still remains moderately common in some areas especially on Barrow Island off the north-west coast of Western Australia.

BELOW   The Quokka is one of the most endearing small macropods. It is common on Rottnest Island near Perth, where it has been intensively studied.

STUDYING MACROPODS

Recently biologists have intensively studied many species of macropod. The resulting research is extremely useful in formulating management plans, particularly in assisting with the conservation of rare and endangered species.

The Bridled Nailtail Wallaby depicted above is wearing a radio collar and ear tag which enable biologists to monitor its movements following release into the wild. Idalia National Park in central Queensland has been chosen as the site for translocation of this endangered species due to the large areas of apparently suitable habitat that have been cleared of sheep. The area also has a history of macropod monitoring and research, and is permanently staffed.

When released, wallabies are fitted with radio collars and intensively followed for the first three days in order to monitor their movements. The presence of a radio collar also results in the increased likelihood of researchers finding any animals which may have died and then identifying the causes of death.

By closely monitoring the movements of released wallabies, biologists are able to establish the types of habitat preferred for feeding and for shelter during the day. Shelter has been shown to be an important factor in avoiding predators such as foxes, feral cats and raptors. Knowledge of the animals whereabouts also aids in retrapping animals to assess reproductive success and body condition, among other factors.

TOP The Bridled Nailtail Wallaby is named after the white 'bridle' which runs across the neck and around the shoulders.
ABOVE   The Northern Nailtail Wallaby remains common throughout much of tropical northern Australia. It feeds on the fresh shoots of green grass, fruits and low herbage.
OPPOSITE This male Bridled Nailtail Wallaby has left its shelter under a bush and is moving into an open area to feed.

TOP The sole survivor of a formerly large group of macropods — the sthenurine kangaroos — the Banded Hare-wallaby is the only macropod to have bars across its back. It is now found only on two islands in Shark Bay.

ABOVE The Mala, or Rufous Hare-wallaby, was formerly widespread across much of central and western Australia. Recently two small colonies of Mala remaining in the Tanami Desert have been wiped out due to predation by foxes and feral cats.

LEFT Breeding throughout the year on the mainland of south-western Australia, the Quokka survives in thickly vegetated swamps and dense gullies — especially in areas of higher rainfall — where it is able to avoid predation by foxes.

ABOVE Common over much of far eastern Australia, the Swamp Wallaby feeds on a wide range of plant foods including both native and introduced species. It is a browsing animal which prefers to feed on shrubs rather than grass.

RIGHT The Swamp Wallaby is a very attractive animal and is easily recognised due to its dark brown fur above, and pale muzzle stripe. When moving through long grass, it frequently makes high leaps and, when moving fast, the head is held low and the tail horizontal.

OPPOSITE Although relatively common, the Swamp Wallaby is a very wary animal, making it difficult to photograph. Breeding may occur all year and the joey remains in the pouch for about 36 weeks. The joey in this photograph has already made short forays from the pouch.

APPENDIX

COMPLETE LIST OF KANGAROOS AND WALLABIES OF AUSTRALIA
SUPERFAMILY MACROPODOIDEA

FAMILY POTOROIDAE

SUBFAMILY HYPSIPRYMNODONTINAE

Musky Rat-kangaroo
Hypsiprymnodon moschatus
Distribution: Tropical rainforest of
northern Queensland

SUBFAMILY POTOROINAE

Rufous Bettong
Aepyprymnus rufescens
Distribution: Grassy forests of
eastern Australia

Tasmanian Bettong
Bettongia gaimardi
Distribution: Grassy woodland of
eastern Tasmania

Burrowing Bettong (Boodie)
Bettongia lesueur
Distribution: Islands off Western
Australia and some introduced sites
of South Australia

Brush-tailed Bettong
Bettongia penicillata
Distribution: Grassy scrub of
south-western Western Australia

Northern Bettong
Bettongia tropica
Distribution: Grassy woodland of
the Lamb Range and Mount
Windsor Tableland, northern Queensland

Long-footed Potoroo
Potorous longipes
Distribution: Dense forests of
East Gippsland, Victoria

Long-nosed Potoroo
Potorous tridactylus
Distribution: Dense forests of far
eastern Australia, and Tasmania

Gilbert's Potoroo
Potorous gilbertii
Distribution: Dense heathland
and scrub of south-western
Western Australia

FAMILY MACROPODIDAE

SUBFAMILY MACROPODINAE

Bennett's Tree-kangaroo
Dendrolagus bennettianus
Distribution: Tropical rainforest
north of Daintree River, Queensland

Lumholtz's Tree-kangaroo
Dendrolagus lumholtzi
Distribution: High-elevation
tropical rainforest south of
Daintree River, Queensland

Spectacled Hare-wallaby
Lagorchestes conspicillatus
Distribution: Tropical grasslands
of Western Australia to
eastern Queensland

Rufous Hare-wallaby (Mala)

Lagorchestes hirsutus
Distribution: Bernier and
Dorre islands off Western Australia

Agile Wallaby

Macropus agilis
Distribution: Grassy woodlands of
tropical coastal Northern Territory,
Queensland and Western Australia

Black-striped Wallaby

Macropus dorsalis
Distribution: Forests and scrub
of eastern Australia

Tammar Wallaby

Macropus eugenii
Distribution: Islands off southern
Western Australia, South Australia
and mainland south-western Western Australia

Western Brush Wallaby

Macropus irma
Distribution: Open forest and scrub
of south-western Western Australia

Parma Wallaby

Macropus parma
Distribution: Dense forests of far
eastern New South Wales

Whiptail Wallaby

Macropus parryi
Distribution: Grassy forests
of eastern Queensland and
north-eastern New South Wales

Red-necked Wallaby

Macropus rufogriseus
Distribution: Forests of eastern
Australia and Tasmania

Eastern Grey Kangaroo

Macropus giganteus
Distribution: Woodland, scrub and
plains of eastern Australia

Western Grey Kangaroo

Macropus fuliginosus
Distribution: Woodland, scrub and
plains of southern Australia

Red Kangaroo

Macropus rufus
Distribution: Woodlands and plains
of central and western Australia

Antilopine Wallaroo

Macropus antilopinus
Distribution: Tropical grassy
woodlands of northern Australia

Common Wallaroo

Macropus robustus
Distribution: Rocky hills of the
Australian mainland

Black Wallaroo

Macropus bernardus
Distribution: Rocky escarpments of
central and western Arnhem Land

Bridled Nailtail Wallaby

Onychogalea fraenata
Distribution: Woodland and scrub
near Dingo and Idalia National Park,
Queensland

Northern Nailtail Wallaby

Onychogalea unguifera
Distribution: Grassy woodland of
tropical northern Australia

Allied Rock-wallaby

Petrogale assimilis

Distribution: Central Queensland, Palm and Magnetic islands

Short-eared Rock-wallaby

Petrogale brachyotis

Distribution: Tropical north of Western Australia and Northern Territory

Monjon (Warabi)

Petrogale burbidgei

Distribution: Kimberley region and nearby islands

Nabarlek

Petrogale concinna

Distribution: Tropical Northern Territory, Kimberley region and adjacent islands

Cape York Rock-wallaby

Petrogale coenensis

Distribution: Eastern Cape York Peninsula, Queensland

Godman's Rock-wallaby

Petrogale godmani

Distribution: Eastern Cape York Peninsula, Queensland

Herbert's Rock-wallaby

Petrogale herberti

Distribution: South-eastern Queensland

Unadorned Rock-wallaby

Petrogale inornata

Distribution: Central coastal Queensland

Black-footed Rock-wallaby

Petrogale lateralis

Distribution: Northern Territory, Western Australia and islands off South Australia

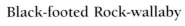

Purple-necked Rock-wallaby

Petrogale lateralis purpureicollis

Distribution: Western Queensland

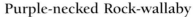

Mareeba Rock-wallaby

Petrogale mareeba

Distribution: Coastal Queensland near Mareeba

Brush-tailed Rock-wallaby

Petrogale penicillata

Distribution: South-eastern Australian mainland

Proserpine Rock-wallaby

Petrogale persephone

Distribution: Small coastal area near Proserpine, Queensland

Rothschild's Rock-wallaby

Petrogale rothschildi

Distribution: Hamersley Range and adjacent islands, Western Australia

Sharman's Rock-wallaby

Petrogale sharmani

Distribution: Coastal ranges near Ingham, Queensland

Yellow-footed Rock-wallaby

Petrogale xanthopus

Distribution: Semi-arid ranges of South Australia, Queensland and New South Wales

Tasmanian Pademelon

Thylogale billardierii
Distribution: Tasmania and
Bass Strait islands

Red-legged Pademelon

Thylogale stigmatica
Distribution: Wet forests of coastal
Queensland and New South Wales

Red-necked Pademelon

Thylogale thetis
Distribution: Wet forests of
coastal New South Wales and
south-eastern Queensland

Quokka

Setonix brachyurus
Distribution: Dense scrub of
south-western Western Australia
and Rottnest Island

Swamp Wallaby

Wallabia bicolor
Distribution: Dense forests of
eastern Australia

SUBFAMILY STHENURINAE

Banded Hare-wallaby

Lagostrophus fasciatus
Distribution: Bernier and Dorre
islands, Western Australia

EXTINCT SPECIES

Desert Rat-kangaroo

Caloprymnus campestris

Broad-faced Potoroo

Potorous platyops

Central Hare-wallaby

Lagorchestes asomatus

Eastern Hare-wallaby

Lagorchestes leporides

Toolache Wallaby

Macropus greyi

Crescent Nailtail Wallaby

Onychogalea lunata

INDEX